This
Treasure Cove Story
belongs to

I AM BELLE

A CENTUM BOOK 978-1-912396-18-4
Published in Great Britain by Centum Books Ltd.
This edition published 2018.

5 7 9 10 8 6 4

Centum Books Ltd, 20 Devon Square, Newton Abbot, Devon, TQ12 2HR, UK.
9/10 Fenian St, Dublin 2, D02 RX24, Ireland.

www.centumbooksltd.co.uk | books@centumbooksltd.co.uk
CENTUM BOOKS Limited Reg.No. 07641486.

A CIP catalogue record for this book is available
from the British Library.

Printed in China.

A Treasure Cove Story

DISNEY
PRINCESS

Beauty and the Beast

I Am Belle

By Andrea Posner-Sanchez
Illustrated by Alan Batson

I am
Belle.

I live in a small
house in a small town.

This is my father, *Maurice*.

He's an **inventor.**

Some of his inventions look a little **strange.** I love that Papa sees things in ways that others don't.

Living in our town is nice, but every day is exactly the same.

I feed the animals...

...tend the gardens

and shop at the markets.

My favourite place to go
is the village bookshop.

I love to read!

I've read all of the books in
the shop – some more than once.

The girls in town think
I'm odd because I'd rather
read than
SWOON...

...over *Gaston*.
They think he's
so handsome.
Gaston agrees!

I can be very brave. When my father went missing, I raced into the woods and found him locked up in a mysterious castle by a creature called the Beast. I offered to take my father's place as the Beast's prisoner.

The castle was a strange and scary place
filled with **talking furniture!** Luckily,
I am good at making new friends.

I met a clock named *Cogsworth*, a candelabrum
named *Lumière*, a teapot named *Mrs Potts*
and her son, *Chip*, a teacup.

I missed my father terribly and was in no mood to eat. But being served delicious food by singing and dancing silverware cheered me right up!

Sometimes I can be too curious for my own good. Even though the Beast told me not to, I went to the West Wing of the castle and saw an *enchanted rose.*

I am comfortable around all creatures,
including little birds,

big

horses...

...and even *enchanted footstools* that act like dogs.

I can bring out the best in people and beasts. Once the Beast's caring nature came out, he became my favourite dance partner.

Thanks to the love I had for the Beast, the curse that had been placed on everyone in his castle was lifted! They all became human again. That chapter of my life was more exciting than any in my favourite books!

Treasure Cove Stories

Please contact Centum Books to receive the full list of titles in the *Treasure Cove Stories* series.
books@centumbooksltd.co.uk

•Book list may be subject to change. Not all titles are listed.